publishers
PAUL ENS and SCOTT CHITWOOD

logo design
STEVE ANDERSON

graphic design
PAUL ENS

NEOZOIC Volume One

This volume collects NEOZOIC #1 through #8 of the comic-book series originally printed by Red 5 Comics.

Published by
RED 5 COMICS
298 Tuscany Vista Rd NW, Calgary, Alberta, Canada, T3L 3B4

www.red5comics.com

To find a comics shop in your area, call the Comic Shop Locator Service toll-free at 1-888-266-4226

Second edition:
ISBN-13: 978-0-9868985-4-9

Printed in Canada.

NeoZoic

SCRIPT
PAUL ENS

ART
J. KORIM

COLORS
JESSIE LAM

LETTERS
TROY PETERI

WWW.RED5COMICS.COM

OVER 588 MILLION KILOMETERS, THE END DESTINATION WOULD VARY BY 380,000 KILOMETERS.

IN THE VASTNESS OF SPACE, 380,000 KILOMETERS IS INSIGNIFICANT.

BUT FOR A RELATIVELY YOUNG LIFE-BEARING PLANET IT IS THE DISTANCE BETWEEN ONE FUTURE...

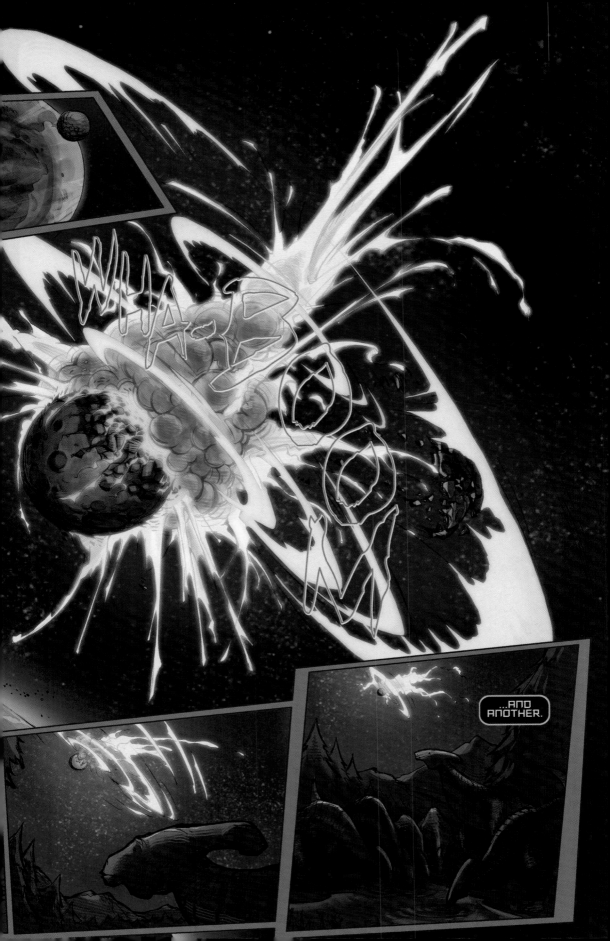

SIXTY-FIVE MILLION YEARS LATER. MONANTI CITY.

YOU DIRECTOR KINNEL?

NO, USE THE NEW IRON-CARBON ALLOY BEAMS THERE. THANKS. LISTEN, IF YOU'RE GOING TO TELL ME ABOUT ANO...

WHOA.

I'M SORRY, CAPTAIN CLAWSON. I DIDN'T...

ACCORDING TO THE MINISTRY SCHEDULE, YOU'RE OUT HERE TWO HOURS EARLY, SON.

AND OLD MEN LIKE CLAW GET GRUMPY IF THEY DON'T GET ENOUGH SLEEP.

I'M SORRY, BUT IF THERE'S ENOUGH MOONLIGHT TO WORK... WE WORK, CAPTAIN.

I DON'T KNOW IF YOU FOLLOWED KING LILAS' LAST ADDRESS. HE PROMISED THAT THIS WALL EXPANSION WOULD BE COMPLETE IN A MONTH. IT'S AT LEAST THREE MONTHS FROM BEING DONE.

WHEN THAT HAPPENS, THEY BRING IN MY TEAM TO CLOSE. IF I MISS THE DATE, THERE ARE NO COMMENDATIONS FOR FOLLOWING PROCEDURE.

I DON'T FOLLOW POLITICS. BUT WHEN CIVILIANS DON'T HAVE ENOUGH COMMON SENSE TO AVOID BECOMING BREAKFAST, THEY BRING IN MY TEAM TO CLOSE. YOU WANT TO STAY ALIVE OUT HERE, YOU RUN EVERYTHING BY ME. GOT IT?

YES, SIR.

COME TO THINK OF IT, HE'S PRETTY MUCH THIS GRUMPY EVEN IF YOU LET HIM SLEEP IN.

WHAT'S THE SQUAD STATUS, LIEUTENANT?

BOVI'S ROUSING THEM. SHOULD BE IN PLACE IN 10 OR 15.

YOU LIKE LONG HOURS, DIRECTOR? SO DO WE. DO THIS RIGHT, AND WE'LL GET ALONG JUST FINE. GO GET ME YOUR PERSONNEL DEPLOYMENT MAP.

UNDERSTOOD.

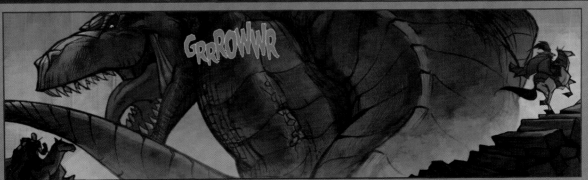

THERE'S NO WATER SOURCE DOWN THERE. WHAT COULD THEY BE DOING?

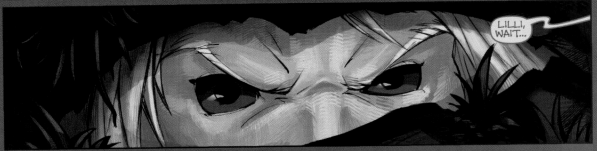

RWO-RWAR

WHISTLE TWEET

GOOD GIRL! LET'S RIDE.

MASTER BAAS, THEY HAVE MILO!

WHAT DO WE DO?

CALM DOWN.

THE TRIALS WERE A SUCCESS. THIS MERELY ACCELERATES OUR PLANS. GET BACK TO BASE...

...AND START THE PREPARATIONS.

DON'T SQUAD! DON'T! SQUAD! CLAW, DO YOU READ ME?

WHAT HAVE YOU DONE, GIRL? EXY CAN'T SPIT OUT TWO WORDS THAT MAKE SENSE.

I'M JUST PAST RING NINE, ALONG SPOKE TEN. I NEED AN OUT AND A DOOR.

THERE'S A HOT-FENCE AT SPOKE NINE-RING SEVEN. IF YOU LIVE THROUGH THAT, YOU HAVE CLEAR SAILING TO THE MAIN QUADRANT DOORS.

TOO PUBLIC. I NEED A SIDE DOOR, MANNED BY SOMEONE WHO OWES YOU A FAVOR AND CAN KEEP THEIR MOUTH SHUT.

YOU USE UP FAVORS FASTER THAN A GOTRO CLEARS A SWINE-PEN.

JUST FIND ME A DOOR AND MEET ME THERE... ALONE.

KATA! THIS IS GOING TO GET UGLY. PETRA, MIND THE CIVILIANS.

MEANWHILE...

GOOD AFTERNOON, CITIZENS OF MONANTI. WELCOME TO STROFI NEWS SQUARE. AS ALWAYS, I'M KYLE ORIAKOS AND THIS IS YOUR THREE-QUARTER LIGHT STROFI NEWS!

WHOOO!

YEAH!

WE LEAD OFF WITH DISSENSION IN KING ULAS' COURT. ULAS' AMBITIOUS WALL EXPANSION PROJECT HAS BEEN APPLAUDED AS VISIONARY BY THOSE CONCERNED WITH CITY OVER-CROWDING, HOUSING SHORTAGES AND SHRINKING FOOD SUPPLIES.

BUT IS OUR DIVINELY APPOINTED LEADER ACTING IN THE WILL OF THE TRIETY? SOURCES WITHIN THE PRIESTHOOD TELL US THAT THE KING AND HIS SPIRITUAL ADVISOR, IRIS MURKO, LOCKED HORNS IN A HEATED BEHIND-CLOSED-DOORS DISCUSSION THAT DEGRADED INTO SHOUTING, THREATS AND THE DESTRUCTION OF SEVERAL CHAIRS.

WHAT COULD MAKE A MEETING OF PRAYER TAKE A VIOLENT TURN? MURKO ACCUSED THE KING OF VIOLATING THE 104TH CHAPTER OF THE LOGOS, WHICH PROHIBITS THE HARVESTING OF THE OUTER FOUR METERS OF ANY CROP OUTSIDE THE CITY WALLS.

KING ULAS IS SAID TO HAVE CALLED THE COMMAND A "SHORT-SIGHTED, LAZY AND WASTEFUL HOLD-OVER FROM A DIFFERENT ERA" AND CONTINUED TO DEMAND NO RESOURCE BE WASTED UNTIL HIS "GLORIOUS LEGACY OF CITY GROWTH" IS COMPLETE.

SOUNDS LIKE THE TRIETY'S FAVORITE SONS COULD BOTH USE A REFRESHER ON CONTROLLING THEIR TEMPER! BUT IRIS ISN'T THE ONLY HOT-HEADED MURKO WE HAVE TODAY, IS IT, LETATH?

THAT'S RIGHT, KYLE. WE HAVE AN EXTRA SPECIAL PREDATOR DEFENSE LEAGUE REPORT TODAY, COURTESY OF YOUNG LILLI MURKO. THE SOPHOMORE HUNTER KEEPS HACKING AND SLASHING HER WAY THROUGH THE RECORD-BOOKS, AND DOING IT WITH STYLE.

YOU'VE SEEN THE TEETH, MEMORIZED THE STATS AND HEARD THE WITNESSES, BUT YOU'RE NOT GOING TO BELIEVE WHAT OUR CAMERA CAUGHT THIS MORNING. IF YOU JUST ATE, YOU MIGHT WANT TO HIDE YOUR EYES, FOLKS!

RAAAH!

AAAH!

BOOOOO

YEAH!

WHOOO!

LI-LLI!
LI-LLI!

RAAAH!

STROFI NEWS BRINGS YOU...THE *TIGRAS SLAYER!*

MURDERERS! MURDERERS!

YOU WANNA BE LUNCH, LIZARD-LOVER?

PDL IS MURDER! ALL THE TRIETY'S CREATURES ARE SACRED! WE HAVE NO RIGHT!

LET'S SEE WHAT THESE HERB-FIENDS SAY OUTSIDE THE WALLS!

SECURITY! SECURITY!

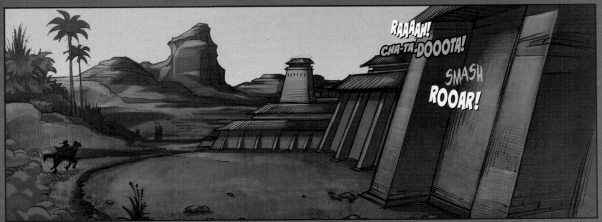

RAAAAH!

CHA-TA-DOOOTA!

SMASH
ROOAR!

WHAT'S WITH ALL THE NOISE INSIDE?

IF I TOLD YOU, THERE'D BE NO DEALING WITH YOUR HUGE HEAD.

WH-WH-WHAT'S THAT?

I THINK SHE'S A TALPID. I PULLED HER FROM THE BIGGEST MESS OF REPTILES I'VE EVER SEEN.

A-A TALPID?! CLAW, YOU NEVER SAID ANYTHING ABOUT BREAKING THE LOGOS! I CAN'T AFFORD TO GO TO HELL RIGHT NOW.

LILLI, YOUR TIGRAS KILL WAS ON THE NEWS. GENERAL TRAGOS IS DEFINITELY GOING TO WANT TO YELL AT US AS SOON AS POSSIBLE. YOU CAN'T ADD HARBORING A STRAY TALPID TO YOUR TROUBLES.

I COULDN'T VERY WELL LEAVE HER OUT THERE.

BETTER OUT THERE THAN IN HERE!

YOU STALL THE GENERAL. WHEN THE SUN GOES DOWN, I'LL TAKE THE GIRL TO MY SISTER.

YOUR... SISTER?

HIGH TEMPLE OF THE TRIETY.

DO YOU WANT TO TALK ABOUT IT, FATHER?

KING ULAS WAS ONCE SMALL IN HIS OWN EYES, BUT NOW HIS OWN HONOR IS ALL HE SEES. I FEAR THE TRIETY HAS REJECTED HIM...

BUT DIDN'T THE TRIETY SPEAK THROUGH YOU TO COMMAND THE KING TO EXPAND THE CITY?

DEAR DAUGHTER, DELIVERING RESULTS IS NOT THE SAME AS OBEDIENCE.

HELLO, CRYSTAL. DAD.

LILLI! THE WHOLE CITY IS LOOKING FOR YOU. WE WERE SO WORRIED...

SAVE YOUR PRAYERS FOR SOMEONE ELSE, I'M FINE. BUT I COULD USE YOUR HELP, CRYSTAL.

MY HELP?

I RESCUED A LITTLE GIRL OUTSIDE THE WALLS TODAY, BUT SHE HAS NO FAMILY OR PLACE TO STAY.

OF COURSE WE CAN TAKE HER. WHERE IS SHE NOW?

WHAT'S LILLI LIKE?

DID YOU GET YOUR OWN SWORD?

DID YOU SEE THAT TIGRAS THIS MORNING? DID YOU HELP KILL IT?

IT WAS GREAT, THANKS. IF YOU COULD EXCUSE ME FOR A MINUTE.

OH, HONEY... WHAT'S THE MATTER?

THEY HATE ME, MOM. I ALMOST GOT EVERYONE KILLED. I CAN'T DO IT. I JUST CAN'T DO IT. IT'S TOO HARD.

SNIFF SNIFF

ROSS, DEAR?

THERE, THERE, SON. YOU'RE HOME. YOU'RE HOME.

WHAT TIME IS OUR SHIFT?

LESS THAN THREE HOURS. WE'RE PROBABLY BETTER OFF JUST STAYING UP.

HE-LLO!

SKREE SKREE

SKREEEEEEE

SKRAAAA

WHAT THE...

CHEW ON THIS, KAZING PITINO!

THERE ARE TOO MANY OF THEM!

THESE THINGS NEVER FLOCK...THEY HATE EACH OTHER.

BOOM

WHOA!

SNORRRT

SKUUUU-REEEEE

WALL CRASH! WALL CRASH! RACHI SQUAD IS UNDER ATTACK. SOUND THE ALARM!

BREEEE BREEEE

BRING THEM!

STOP IT! STOP IT! *JUST, STOP IT!*

I'M SORRY YOU'VE STIRRED, KING ULAS. IT'S THE PREDATOR DEFENSE LEAGUE GENERAL SIREN.

IT HAS NOT BEEN SO LONG THAT I'VE FORGOTTEN THE SOUND, SKEP. WHAT IS THE SITUATION?

OTHER THAN THE WINGED ARIAL ATTACK, THERE ARE SEVERAL REPORTS OF WALL COLLISIONS. IT IS LIKELY SOME SORT OF MIGRATIONAL ANOMALY, BUT IT WOULD BE PRUDENT TO GET YOU TO A SAFE CELLAR.

NO! I WILL NOT RUN. SEND FOR MY UNIFORM FROM STORAGE, THEN GET MY WIFE AND CHILDREN TO SAFETY.

BUT YOUR MAJESTY, MY SWORN DUTY IS TO YOUR SAFETY. IF ANYTHING WERE TO...

IF YOU SERVE ME, THEN UNDERSTAND THAT I AM TRUSTING YOU WITH WHAT MATTERS TO ME MOST...MY FAMILY. KEEP THEM SAFE. DO NOT WORRY ABOUT ME.

BUT HIGHNESS, THE PDL...

SKEP, I'M COUNTING ON YOU. GO.

Y-YES, YOUR MAJESTY.

THE FATE OF A MILLION RESTS ON YOUR ACTIONS THIS DAY. BE STRONG AND COURAGEOUS, FOR THE TRIETY IS WITH YOU.

EVERY LIZARD IN WALKING DISTANCE IS AT OUR DOORSTEP, PEOPLE. FOR ONCE, THE CARNIVORES ARE OUR ALLIES, THINNING THE HERD. IT'S THE PLANT EATERS SCARING THE CITIZENS AND CRACKING THE PAINT.

ALL SQUADS NOT BOLSTERING AIR DEFENSE ARE TO BEGIN IMMEDIATE EXTRA-PERIMETER SWEEPS. ELIMINATE EVERYTHING BIGGER THAN A TRACHIMAKROS. GOOD HUNTING!

GO OUTSIDE AND SLAUGHTER BLUNT-TEETH? THEY SERIOUS?

YOU CAN'T FORTIFY A POSITION FROM THE OUTSIDE.

TRY NOT TO GET HURT OUT THERE, CLAWSON. I'LL BE HUNTING... NO TIME FOR AN OLD-MAN RESCUE MISSION.

DON'T SQUAD, MOVE OUT!

HEAVEN IS PUNISHING US!

PRIEST MURKO MUST BE RIGHT... THE KING HAS SINNED AGAINST THE TRIETY.

SOMEONE'S BROKEN THE LOGOS. WE HAVE TO FIND OUT WHO, BEFORE WE ALL DIE.

THESE ARE TIMES FOR FAITH, NOT BLAME.

DEPARTMENT OF THE PERIMETER

WAIT HERE.

AND HOW DID I KNOW YOU'D BE IN, DIRECTOR KINNEL?

CAPTAIN CLAWSON! YOU CAN, UM...CALL ME PAX. WHAT, ER...WHAT CAN I DO FOR YOU?

WHERE'S THE WALL COMING DOWN, PAX?

THE PERIMETER CAN WITHSTAND THE ADVANCES OF A CONFUSED MALE TACHIMAKROS IN HEAT. WE'RE PERFECTLY...

THIS IS WAY TOO MUCH MATH FOR SOMEONE WHO THINKS WE'RE GOING TO BE FINE.

LAST TIME. WHERE IS IT GOING TO BREAK?

OK, OK. I'M WORRIED ABOUT NORTHWEST SECTION 84. OFFICIALLY, THE ENTIRE WALL WAS RETROFIT EIGHT YEARS AGO FOR SEVERAL KILOTONNES OF TENSILE PRESSURE.

OFF THE RECORD, THE KING PULLED RESOURCES FOR HIS EXPANSION PROJECT AND SOME OLDER SECTIONS HAVEN'T BEEN UPGRADED YET. FOUR TRACHIMAKROS ARE CRASHING THE AREA. THEY'LL BE THROUGH IN AN HOUR...MAYBE LESS.

TAKE ME!

HURRY UP, BOVI!

C'MON, PLEO. YOU KNOW I'M ALLERGIC TO EFAUNT HAIR!

YOU'RE THE ONE WHO LET MY SKALAS RUN OFF.

AAA-CHOO!

THIS IS IT.

TAKE YOUR POSITIONS, DONTI SQUAD. THIS IS HAPPENING NOW!

HERE.

WHAT'S THIS?

YOU MIGHT AS WELL MAKE YOURSELF USEFUL.

FIRE!

KA-SHING

KA-SHING

BWWWWAAAAH!

THUMP

CONCENTRATE ON THE CARNIVORES! LOOK FOR POINTY TEETH!

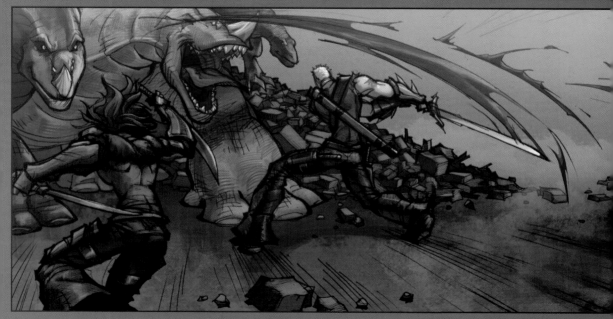

OH NO, THE MELAPSOS' HOUSE.

MOM, DAD... WE'VE GOTTA GO, NOW!

ROSS, DON'T WORRY ABOUT US. YOU'RE PREDATOR DEFENSE LEAGUE NOW, YOUR PLACE IS WITH YOUR SQUAD.

FORGET PDL, I NEED TO GET YOU...

SQUASH.

MOM?! DAD?! NO!

EEEE-AAH!

SKEPP!

KING ULAS?! I'M SO HAPPY TO...

SKEP, WHY ARE YOU HERE? WHERE ARE MY FAMILY?

WE WERE SEPARATED, YOUR HIGHNESS. THE PRINCE AND PRINCESS WENT TOWARD STROFI NEWS SQUARE, BUT I WAS CUT OFF FROM FOLLOWING.

PDL! TO STROFI SQUARE TO FIND MY CHILDREN. LET'S MOVE OUT!

I'M SORRY! I'VE FAILED YOU.

HOPE YOU HAVEN'T.

WHAT'S UP, CAPTAIN?

THEY'RE NOT HUNGRY. IGNORING THE PORCINE.

THEN WHERE ARE THEY GOING?

THE TEMPLE.

DAD! CRYSTAL!

THEY'RE AFTER THE GIRL, LILLI. WHAT HAVE YOU DONE?

MY DAUGHTER. OH, MY PRECIOUS DAUGHTER...

OH, DAD.

YOU DID THIS, CHILD. TAKE THAT CREATOR-LESS ABOMINATION AND GET OUT OF THIS TEMPLE!

DAD... NO!

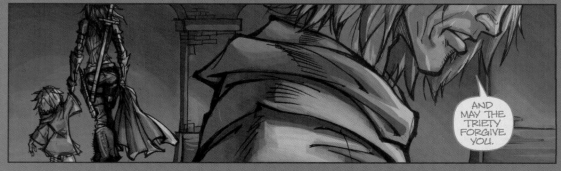

AND MAY THE TRIETY FORGIVE YOU.

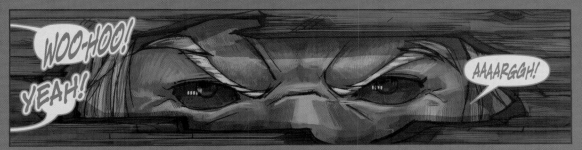

‹NO SIGN OF THE PRINCE AND PRINCESS, AND THE GREAT LIZARDS HAVE ALL LEFT THE CITY, MASTER.›

THEY MUST HAVE KILLED THE LITTLE GIRL. PITY, I HAD MORE USE FOR HER. NEVERTHELESS, THIS ONLY ACCELERATES OUR PLANS.

KLANK

THE WALLS OF MY NEW CITY ARE FALLING APART, ULAS. YOU DIDN'T TAKE CARE OF IT FOR ME. TSK. TSK. BUT I'M SURE YOUR CITIZENS WILL BE HAPPY TO ASSIST IN THE REPAIR.

ROUSE THEM! WITH WHIPS!

〈MASTER BAAS, WHY DO YOU KEEP THE PRIEST AND THE KING ALIVE, DEFILING YOUR NEW THRONE ROOM?〉

〈ULAS MUST TASTE HIS DEFEAT, AND SUFFER MUCH MORE BEFORE HE CAN BE ALLOWED TO DIE..〉

〈WHAT WORD FROM THE SCOUTS?〉

NO ONE CAN BE OUTSIDE AFTER SUNDOWN. THE MEGASAVRAS WILL....

OH, A FEW OF YOUR PEOPLE WILL BE EATEN, YES. BUT YOU MUST ALL LEARN TO WORK AT NIGHT, IF YOU ARE TO SERVICE US.

WHY ARE YOU DOING THIS, TALPID SCUM?

WHY? WHY INDEED.

HAVE YOU SEEN CLAW? ANYONE FROM DONTI SQUAD?

NO, JUST YOU... BUT IT SEEMS LIKE HALF THE PREDATOR DEFENSE LEAGUE IS HERE.

HOLD ON. THAT'S LILLI'S DAD.

PRIEST MURKO! PRIEST MURKO! IT'S PLEO, FROM DONTI SQUAD.

HAVE YOU SEE LILLI? IS SHE ALL RIGHT?

BOTH MY DAUGHTERS ARE DEAD.

OH NO!

LILLI...

WATCH THIS. NOTICE THEY NEVER SPEAK TO EACH OTHER.

BUT THERE'S CLEARLY SOME KIND OF COMMAND HIERARCHY AT WORK.

FREAKY, HUH? NO HAND SIGNALS OR ANYTHING.

IT'S GENERALLY ACCEPTED THAT THE TALPID SURVIVE BY HIDING FROM THE BIG PREDATORS, BE IT IN SHELTERS OR UNDERGROUND. NATURALLY, VERBAL COMMUNICATION WOULD BE A BAD IDEA BECAUSE THEY'D GIVE AWAY THEIR POSITION. BUT...WHAT IF THEY DEVELOPED SOME KIND OF TELEPATHY TO LET THEM TALK TO EACH OTHER IN COMPLETE SILENCE?

SOUNDS PRETTY FAR-FETCHED.

BUT IT WOULD MAKE SENSE, RIGHT?

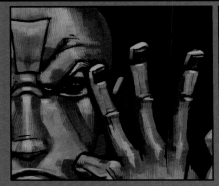

SLASH SLASH

WHERE DID YOU GET THIS SWORD?!

TOO BLEE A NY?

MORNING. DENTRO WOODS.

MMMMM, LILLI. THAT FEELS SO GOOD.

WHAT DID YOU SAY?

AAAGGH!

SERPENTES! I HATE SERPENTES!

I SEE OUR SITUATION HASN'T IMPROVED.

NO, BUT THE GIRL IS CALM SO I DON'T THINK WE'RE IN IMMEDIATE DANGER. STILL, IF YOU HAVE ANY IDEAS FOR AN ESCAPE PLAN...BY ALL MEANS.

TOO FAR BACK TO THE CITY ON FOOT.

WAIT. WHAT'S THAT?

I'M NOT MAD AT YOU, PSARI. IT ALL WORKED OUT FOR THE BEST. I WAS NEVER ONE FOR TAKING ORDERS. "YES, SIR" EVERY DAY...THAT'S NOT FOR ME. BESIDES, IF I WERE PDL I'D BE DEAD OR IN A HOLDING CELL TODAY, JUST LIKE YOUR FRIENDS.

I DON'T NEED MONEY OR GLORY... HERE, I AM QUEEN!

WHO ARE THESE PEOPLE?

THE LOST, ORPHANS, DOWNTRODDEN, THE NOT-QUITE-GOOD-ENOUGH-FOR-DADDY. ANYONE WITH NO PLACE TO GO. THE PEOPLE THE TEMPLE USED TO CARE ABOUT.

TOGETHER WE FIND FOOD, SHELTER, HOPE, COMMUNITY, ACCEPTANCE. NO RULES, EXCEPT ONE...EVERYONE CONTRIBUTES.

CONTRIBUTES HOW?

OH, ROSS-Y. I WOULDN'T WANT TO SULLY THAT CLEAN PERFECTLY-TRAINED MIND OF YOURS WITH THOSE KIND OF DETAILS.

YOU'RE CRIMINALS?

MONANTI GAVE UP ON US, PSARI. WE DON'T OWE THEM ANYTHING.

RUSTLE
RUSTLE

CAPTAIN!

CLAW? CAN YOU HEAR ME? WHAT HAPPENED?

PETRA? PETRA. I...SHE.... I....

THE TALPID HAVE TAKEN OVER THE CITY. WE'VE GOT TO GET YOU OUT OF HERE. LET ME HELP YOU UP.

PETRA. LISTEN. MY SPINE IS BROKEN. I CAN'T FEEL MY LEGS. YOU CAN'T LET ME DIE HIDING. PUT ME OUTSIDE FOR A HUNTER'S DEATH.

WITH ALL DUE RESPECT, CAPTAIN...YOU TAUGHT US TO IGNORE THE TRADITIONS OF THE OLD WARRIORS.

LILLI.

LILLI? IS SHE ALIVE?

LILLI DID THIS...TO ME. TO US. SHE BROUGHT THE MEGASAVROS. THE TALPID. DESTRUCTION.

SHE MUST...BE.... STOPPED.

HERE YOU GO, SWEETIE.

CAN YOU EVEN IMAGINE? TORTURED FROM BIRTH AS PART OF THIS BAAS-GUY'S TELEPATHIC WEAPON EXPERIMENTS.

SHE SEEMS PRETTY NORMAL, ALL THINGS CONSIDERED.

WHAT ARE WE GOING TO DO WITH HER? WE CAN'T GIVE HER BACK TO THE TALPID, WE CAN'T TAKE HER BACK TO MONANTI CITY, AND WE CAN'T JUST LEAVE HER HERE.

WE'RE GOING TO NEED TO FIND OUT MORE ABOUT THIS TELEPATHY OF HERS. WHY DO THE SAVROS RESPOND TO IT?

MILO, BODA KOO NU TEECHA, REE?

BOODOO FI NA TEA, ONGOK TIMORTO. BO FILA MON KANG WOO KAY.

WHEN SHE'S SCARED AND ALONE, THEY KEEP HER SAFE.

THEY'RE NOT JUST FOLLOWING? THEY'RE RESPONDING TO HER.

PAX, ASK MILO TO TELL THE PITINO TO COVER ITS EYES.

MILO, CHOKTEE EN PITINO MATI KALY.

THREE NIGHTS LATER.

‹AS YOU CAN SEE, MASTER BAAS, THEY HIT US AGAIN. ALL THE REPAIRS FROM LAST NIGHT HAVE BEEN RIPPED APART.›

‹COULD IT BE THE GREAT LIZARDS, MASTER?›

‹NO, THEN THE FOOD STORES WOULD BE SWARMED. MILO MUST STILL BE ALIVE SOMEWHERE, KEEPING THEM AT BAY. IT'S MONTANTI VERMIN SOMEHOW ELUDING US.›

‹I WANT DAYLIGHT GUARDS POSTED AT ALL THE CONSTRUCTION SITES!›

‹BUT, MASTER, MY CREW CANNOT STAND IN THE LIGHT ALL DAY. THEY'D NEVER...›

I KNOW WHO YOU ARE, MISS KOINO. REPORTER FOR STRONTI NEWS.

THANK YOU, SIR. CALL ME ANNA. AND YOU ARE?

I'M BOVI. THIS IS PLEO.

DON'T SQUAD. PREDATOR DEFENSE LEAGUE.

YOU'RE PDL? YIKES. MOST OF THE PDL HATES ME.

THAT'S HOW WE KNOW WHO YOU ARE.

WHI-CRACK

I SAID BACK TO WORK!

WE TALPID CARE ONLY ABOUT THE PRESENT, AND THE FUTURE. WE DO NOT CLING TO OR CELEBRATE THE PAST LIKE YOU MONANTI DO.

BUT STILL, SOME STORIES ARE PASSED ON, WHISPERED AT DUSK BETWEEN THE HUNTS OF THE DAY AND FEAR OF THE NIGHT. STORIES OF THE ABOVE-GROUNDERS FOR GENERATION AFTER GENERATION.

LEGENDS OF CRUEL WARRIORS. WHISPERS OF RICHES. QUESTIONS ABOUT THEIR DISDAIN. EVEN TALES OF BENEVOLENCE.

YET IN MY LIFE, KING ULAS-- IN YOUR REIGN-- THE MONANTI HAVE GONE FROM INDIFFERENT BENEFACTORS TO USURPERS OF RESOURCES AND DICTATORS OF THE LAND.

YOU TAKE MORE AND MORE. TALPID WOMEN AND CHILDREN HAVE HAD TO EXPOSE THEMSELVES LONGER TO GATHER LESS AND LESS. THE GREAT LIZARDS GROWING FAT ON THE BODIES OF MY KIN.

I SAW YOU ONCE, ULAS... MANY YEARS AGO.

WHO'S DOING THIS?

CAPTAIN MITCH CLAWSON. HE'S NOT ACCOUNTED FOR.

LIMA, HOW COULD YOU?

IF IT'S CLAWSON, YOU'RE PROBABLY LOOKING FOR HIS PROTEGE, LILLI MURKO. SHE'S THE PRIEST'S DAUGHTER.

⟨MASTER BAAS, IT'S THE GIRL WHO TOOK MILO FROM THE VALLEY.⟩

SHE'S THE ONE. HOW DO WE DISCREDIT HER?

I HAVE JUST THE THING.

OKAY, THAT SHOULD DO IT.

MY SISTERS MADE ME PLAY WITH DOLLS. THEY'D BE SO PROUD.

LET'S GIVE IT A TRY.

CHA POKO UTMAN DISA, MILO. TOLPA DA PONKI NU PUTI CHA NAGA.

FEELS LIKE RIGHT ABOUT HERE.

REED-- THIS IS RIDICULOUS. WE'RE THE PRINCESS AND PRINCE OF MONANTI. WE'VE BEEN IN THE WOODS FOLLOWING THIS KID FOR DAYS. WE DON'T KNOW WHERE OUR PARENTS ARE AND I NEED A BATH.

THE CITY'S BEEN TAKEN OVER BY TALPID, LASHANNA. WE CAN'T GO WALKING IN THE PALACE....THEY WANT TO KILL US. BESIDES, I LIKE HIM. AND HE SEEMS TO HAVE A PLAN.

YOU HAVE A PLAN, DON'T YOU, AVIDE?

ABSOLUTELY.

WHAT IS IT?

STRONTI
NEWS
SQUARE.

...THEY HAVE EVERYONE IN THE SQUARE.

PEOPLE OF MONANTI, I AM ANNA KOINO, FORMERLY OF STRONTI NEWS.

YOU DESPISE AND FEAR OUR NEW MASTERS, THE TALPID. YOU ARE ANGRY AT THE TRIETY, IF HE EXISTS, FOR BETRAYING US. AND YOU ARE RIGHT TO FEEL THIS WAY.

BUT MASTER BAAS, NEW LEADER OF MONANTI, HAS SHOWN COMPASSION ON US, AND ALLOWED ME TO ADDRESS YOU TODAY. FOR WHILE THE TALPID NOW RULE, IT WAS OUR ENEMY WITHIN THAT BROUGHT US TO SLAVERY TODAY.

CLAW, YOU'LL WANT TO SEE THIS.

IT WAS A CONSPIRACY OF THE CHURCH, THE PALACE AND THE PREDATOR DEFENSE LEAGUE TO BETRAY US TO THEIR OWN END.

ALL THREE SAT IN RULE OVER YOU... BETTER THAN YOU... IN AUTHORITY, TELLING YOU WHAT TO DO, HOW TO WORSHIP AND HOW TO LIVE.

I GIVE YOU LILLI MURKO -- HONORED BY THE KING, THE VAUNTED STAR OF THE PDL, AND DAUGHTER OF THE HIGH PRIEST HIMSELF. IT WAS LILLI, IN HER ARROGANCE, WHO LAUNCHED AN ATTACK IN THE WOODS AND STOLE A LITTLE TALPID GIRL FROM HER FAMILY. IN DEFIANCE OF EVERY LAW AND TRADITION, MURKO BROUGHT THE CHILD INTO MONANTI CITY... DEFILING EVEN THE HIGH TEMPLE.

IT WAS THIS CHILD, IN A DESPERATE CRY OF HELP TO BE FREED OF LILLI THE KIDNAPPER, WHO CALLED THE MEGASAVROS TO THE CITY. THE GREAT LIZARDS HEARD HER CALL AND DESTROYED THE WALLS IN THE GIRL'S DEFENSE.

THE TALPID FOLLOWED -- IN ACCORDANCE WITH THEIR JUST LAWS TO WIN BACK THEIR STOLEN KIN. WHO AMONG US WOULD NOT GO TO WAR FOR OUR CHILDREN?

SHE'S RIGHT.

THE COWARD LILLI MURKO HAS FLED WITH MILO, OUR DAUGHTER. BUT WE HAVE HERE YOUR TRAITORS -- HER MENTORS, HER KING...AND HER FATHER.

WHAT IS YOUR PENALTY FOR TREASON?

SWIP

WHACK

GO GO GO!

DADDY!

LASHANNA!

FATHER! THIS WAY!

LOOK OUT BEHIND YOU!

THIS WAY, YOUR HIGHNESS.

DADDY, YOU'RE ALRIGHT.

TIME TO COME BACK INSIDE, YOUR HIGHNESSES.

I DON'T THINK SO.

HE IS THE ONE YOU PROMISED.

BRUMMMBLE

KATA-KAZA, IT'S LILLI!

PETRA, FIND ME A HORSE.... AND A LOT OF ROPE.

‹MASTER BAAS, SHE HAS THE GIRL. SHE IS DELIBERATELY DRAWING THE GREAT LIZARDS BACK TO THE CITY. IF SHE GETS INSIDE, THEY WILL DESTROY THE WALLS AGAIN.›

‹IT'S TOO BAD WE JUST KILLED MONANTI'S BEST REPTILE HUNTERS.›

‹YES, THAT *IS* TOO BAD, ISN'T IT?›

‹SEND MEN TO THE HUNTER'S HALL TO GATHER EVERY WEAPON AND TAKE THEM TO THE PRISON. I WILL NOT LOSE MY CITY.›

WHAT'S GOING ON?

I DON'T KNOW, BUT I'M IMAGINING A FEW PLACES TO PUT THIS SWORD.

YOU WERE ONCE CALLED "PREDATOR DEFENSE" AND I AM CALLING YOU TO BE THIS ONCE AGAIN. THE GREAT REPTILES WHO DESTROYED HALF OF MONANTI ARE COMING BACK TO FINISH THE TASK.

YOUR JOB IS THE SAME AS IT HAS ALWAYS BEEN... KEEP THE GREAT LIZARDS OUT OF THE CITY.

IF YOU FAIL, THE CITIZENS BEHIND YOU WILL DIE. IT IS MONANTI, NOT TALPID, WHOSE FLESH WILL FEED THE MEAT EATERS AND STAIN THE FEET OF THE LEAF EATERS.

AND TO PREPARE YOU... IT IS THE TRAITOR LILLI MURKO WHO IS BRINGING THE BEASTS.

LILLI'S ALIVE?

SHE MAY HAVE BEEN ONE OF YOU, BUT DO NOT FORGET THAT SHE IS THE INSTRUMENT OF YOUR DESTRUCTION.

DON'T WORRY ABOUT LILLI.

CLAW?

CAPTAIN?

YOU REALLY ARE A BOY SCOUT, AREN'T YOU?

WE CAN'T HELP LILLI IF WE DON'T KNOW THE PLAN.

NENOVI FRUIT. THAT JUST DOESN'T MAKE ANY SENSE.

UM, LOOK UP, PSARI.

OH. ALL.... RIGHT.

LET'S GET THE WORD OUT.

SHE'S NOT GOING TO HURT ANYONE WITH MELONS.

FORGET THE PAYLOAD... LILLI'S FOUND A WAY TO CONTROL THE MEGASAVROS.

IS THIS GOING TO WORK, LILLI?

〈MASTER BAAS, WE'VE STARTED EVACUATION OF THE MONANTI FOOD STORES INTO THE TUNNELS. WHAT ARE YOUR ORDERS?〉

〈THEY WILL NOT USE MY CREATION AGAINST ME..〉

MILO!

I'M ALIVE, LILLI. YOU BROKE ME, BUT YOU DIDN'T KILL ME. I'VE COME TO FINISH IT BEFORE ANYONE ELSE GETS HURT. THE CHILD MUST DIE.

OH, CLAW. WHAT HAVE I DONE?

TEE-YAH!

WALLMAKER?! IS THAT YOU?

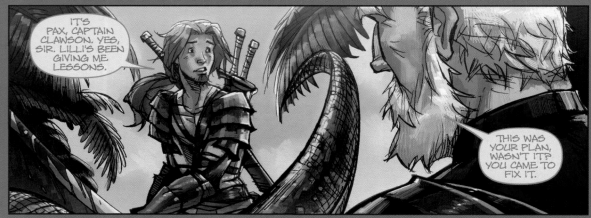

IT'S PAX, CAPTAIN CLAWSON. YES, SIR. LILLI'S BEEN GIVING ME LESSONS.

THIS WAS YOUR PLAN, WASN'T IT? YOU CAME TO FIX IT.

BAAS IS PROBABLY IN THE PALACE. GO FINISH THIS THING, SOLDIER. FOR ME.

LOOKS LIKE WE'RE BACK IN THE REPTILE KILLING BUSINESS.

YES, SIR.

MONANTI ROYAL THRONE ROOM

BANG

YOU KNOW, MISS MURKO, THE PRIMARY FUNCTION OF TALPID TELEPATHY IS TO WARN EACH OTHER OF DANGER.

IT'S MY PRIMARY FUNCTION TO BE DANGER, SO NATURE IS WORKING ITSELF OUT.

THANK YOU, CAPTAIN!

AND WITHOUT YOU, I WOULDN'T HAVE MY CITY BACK.

THANK YOU, *GENERAL* CLAWSON...NEW COMMANDER OF THE PREDATOR DEFENSE LEAGUE.

I'M NOT YOUR MAN, ULAS. I'M BROKEN. THE ONLY REASON I'M STILL UPRIGHT ON THIS HORSE IS THAT I'VE BEEN TIED HERE.

IT'S NOT YOUR LEGS I NEED, CAPTAIN. IT'S YOUR MIND, YOUR EXPERIENCE. WHILE I REBUILD THIS CITY, YOU NEED TO REBUILD THE PDL.

THE END

THE ART OF NEOZOIC

Also available from Red 5 Comics...

Atomic Robo and the Fightin' Scientists of Tesladyne
ISBN: 978-0-9809302-0-7

Atomic Robo and the Dogs of War
ISBN: 978-0-9809302-2-1

Atomic Robo and the Shadow from Beyond Time
ISBN: 978-0-9809302-5-2

Atomic Robo and Other Strangeness
ISBN: 978-0-9809302-8-3

Atomic Robo and the Deadly Art of Science
ISBN: 978-0-9809302-4-5

Atomic Robo and the Ghost of Station X
ISBN: 978-0-9868985-0-1

Atomic Robo and the Flying She-Devils of the Pacific
ISBN: 978-0-9868985-2-5

Atomic Robo presents Real Science Adventures
ISBN: 978-0-9868985-1-8

Abyss: Volume One
Surprise! Your dad's a super villain.
ISBN: 978-0-9809302-1-4

Box 13
Deadly noir delivered.
ISBN: 978-0-9809302-6-9

We Kill Monsters
Rednecks out for blue blood.
ISBN: 978-0-9809302-7-6

Zombies of Mass Destr
Let the dead handle the M
ISBN: 978-0-9809302-9